THE WILDS

1. GONE

Alone, I am petrified

you'll see her grow in me.

I cannot conjure her name.

Her vacancy
is something I cannot bear.

2.
WHAT
REMAINS

3. RUNAWAY

the ache

the tired breaths

past

the ocean, along the sand,

I hope one day you'll understand.

4. CONSTELLATIONS

5. I HAVE HEARD
THESE VOICES BEFORE

6. THESE ARE THE WILDS

The Hill

paws and feet

a path is worn

into a decision

The Field

seeds sleep
shoots reach
a new universe blooms

7. FEED

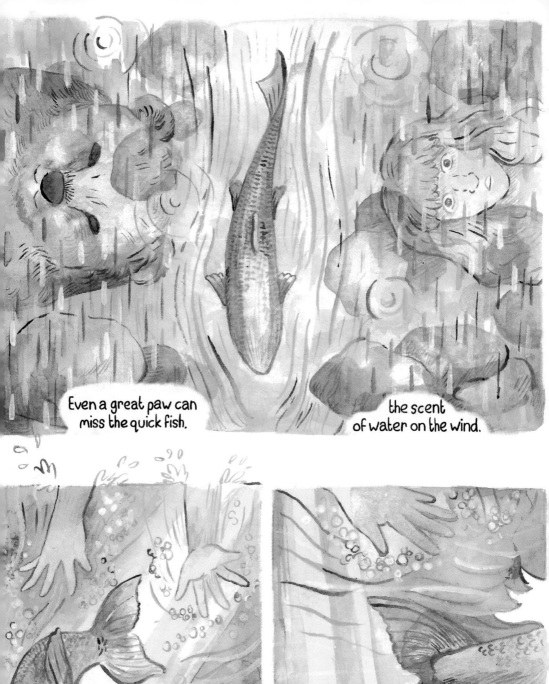

Even a great paw can
miss the quick fish.

the scent
of water on the wind.

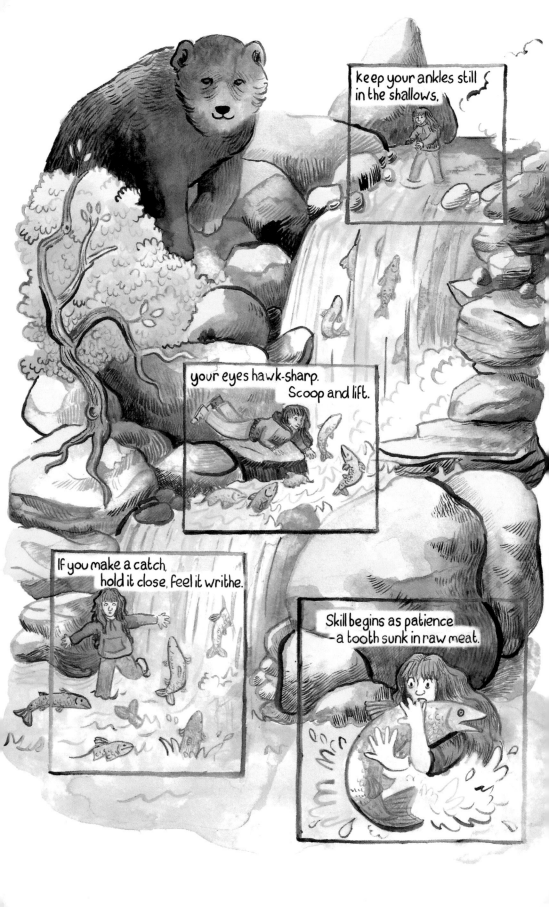

8. DEEP WALK

walk quiet, moonlight

trees bend, white

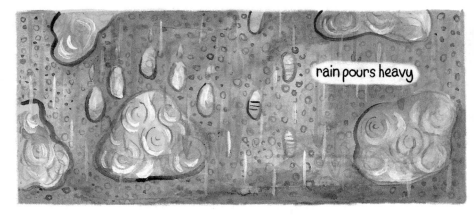

rain pours heavy

on bowed heads

fox and cuckoo

worm and soil

bones on bones

not to forget

the day's promise

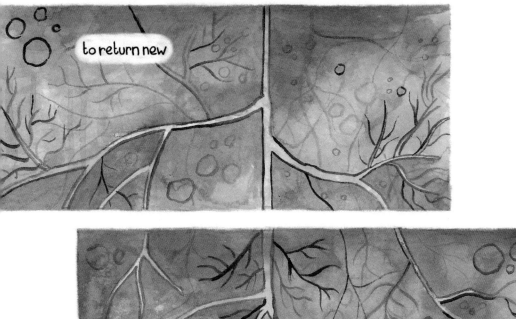

to return new

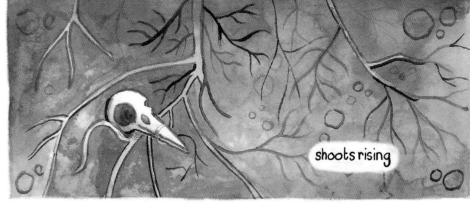

shoots rising

through brown leaves

9. CLIMB

We bears make slow steps.
Take a breath, a firm grip, honey
never spoils. The bees will sting
to protect their queen
as she multiplies
But you must climb.
A bear's fur grows thick
over time, we learn to listen
to the hive's hum,
to interpret the bees' dance
to know which branches hold
and which will fall.

Remember:
each step
brings you
closer

10. THE DARK

11. WE ALL RETURN

like a mother, I have given everything: rain to river, stone to hill, seed to roots.

Though I do not wish it, I must go –

like the deer, the forest draws me back.

And you must return to the places you knew:

to the light of your people, the fire of home.

12. WAYS BACK

many curtains tweaked and blinds closed, many dried

faces and folded handkerchiefs. Some

bury their pains with pride,

but I carry them inside.

The morning is a long weathered line, but our lips widen.

we apologise, eat honeyed oats.
It feels good to be home.

There are many ways
to live, to love and die.

I hold him bear-close
and whisper: we can
carry them inside.

There are many ways to hide.

13. IN FLIGHT

Your timbre in our heads, we hum goodbyes like hopeful songbirds, beat our wings and run to sing your name on our long migration.

Russell Jones was the UK's first Pet Poet Laureate. He has published ten books (poetry and novels), hundreds of poems and dozens of stories. Russell has edited three writing anthologies, is deputy editor of science fiction magazine Shoreline of Infinity, and has a PhD in Creative Writing from The University of Edinburgh.

Aimee Lockwood is an illustrator and comic maker based in the far north of Scotland, where she likes to get lost in nature and stare at the stars. You can find more of her work at www.aimeelockwood.co.uk

Thank you to Creative Scotland, and to all of our kickstarter backers for their support and encouragement! Our thanks also to Child Bereavement UK and their team of readers for their invaluable feedback.

Published in 2021 by Tapsalteerie
9 Anderson Terrace, Tarland
Aberdeenshire, AB34 4YH
www.tapsalteerie.co.uk

978-1-9162148-4-2

Printed and bound by Comic Printing UK

The creators acknowledge support from Creative Scotland towards the development of this title.

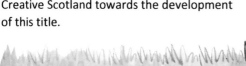